CONTENTS

™

THE NEW

BATMAN
ADVENTURES

Published by Pedigree books Limited
Beech Hill House, Walnut Gardens, Exeter, Devon EX4 4DH
E-mail books@pedigreegroup.co.uk
Published 2005

ROGUES GALLERY

Can you colour these pictures to match the artwork in the rogues gallery?

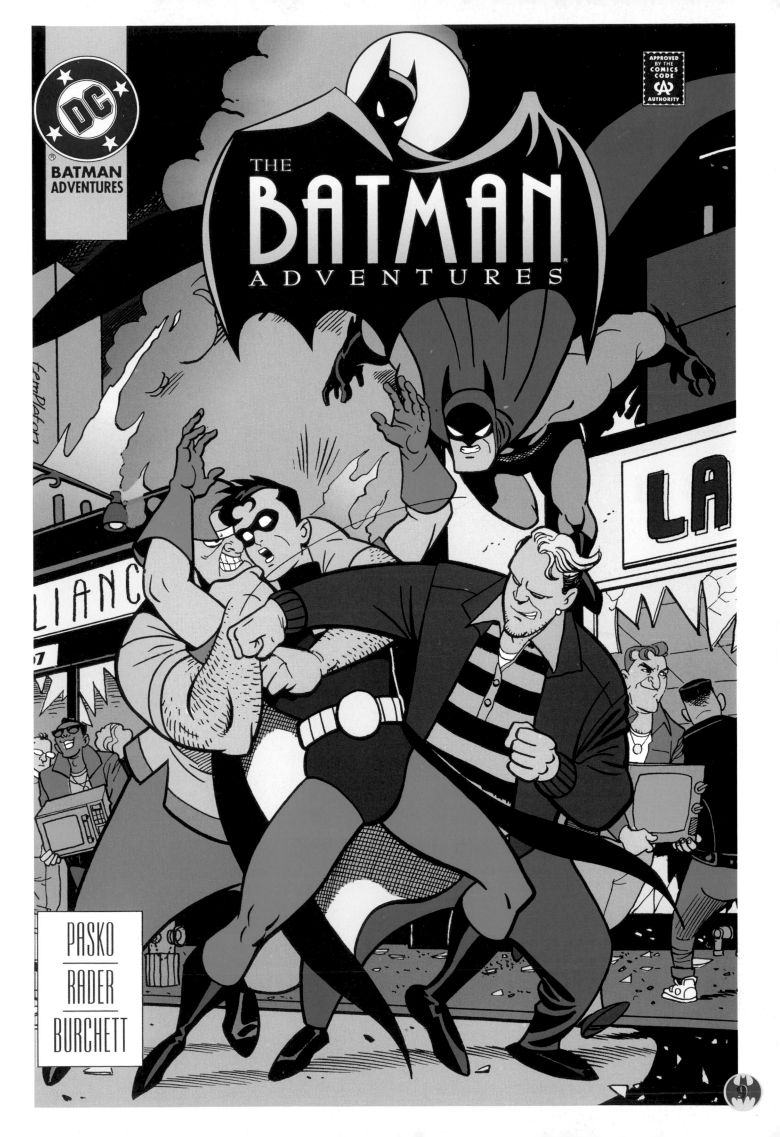

ACT ONE:
PANIC IN THE STREETS

RIOT ACT

WRITTEN BY MARTIN PASKO PENCILLED BY BRAD RADER INKED BY RICK BURCHETT
COLORED BY RICK TAYLOR LETTERED BY TIM HARKINS EDITED BY SCOTT PETERSON

BATMAN CREATED BY BOB KANE

KCHONK

YAAAH!

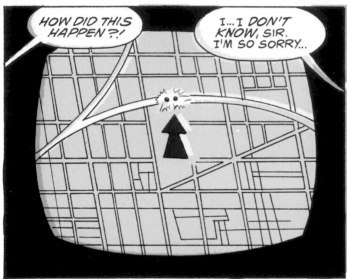

HOW DID THIS HAPPEN?!

I...I DON'T KNOW, SIR. I'M SO SORRY...

...I--I MUST HAVE GIVEN HILLBORO-141 THE WRONG SWITCHING-INSTRUCTIONS...!

SOMETHING... SOMETHING HAPPENED TO ME... SOMETHING WEIRD--IN MY BRAIN--I...I DON'T KNOW HOW TO EXPLAIN IT...!

BUT I TRIED TO COMPENSATE... I...I THOUGHT I WAS REMEMBER-ING THE CORRECT ROUTING SEQUENCE--

CORBETT

"REMEMBERING"? GOOD GOD, WHAT'S WRONG WITH YOU, MAN?

ALL THE DATA IS RIGHT THERE ON YOUR SCREEN! COULDN'T YOU READ IT?

I SAID, COULDN'T YOU READ IT?!

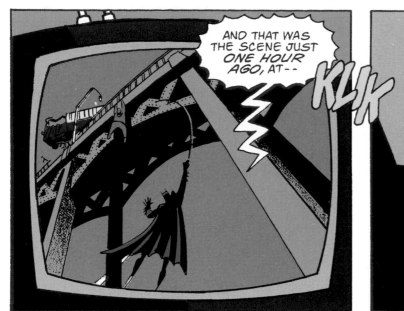

AND THAT WAS THE SCENE JUST *ONE HOUR AGO*, AT--

KLIK

MARIO...THIS FRIEND OF YOURS --THIS MISTER...

CORBETT, PROFESSOR. *BARNEY CORBETT.*

WHATEVER. YOU *DID* GIVE THIS CORBETT FELLOW THE *GIFT,* DIDN'T YOU?

YESSIR.

AND YOU'RE *SURE* HE TOOK IT TO WORK WITH HIM?

YES, PROFESSOR.

THEN WE CAN *ASSUME* IT'S SAFE TO CALL OUR TEST OF THE *DYSLEXUS DEVICE* A *SUCCESS.*

IN THAT CASE... SET *PHASE ONE* OF OUR PLAN IN MOTION *IMMEDIATELY.*

THIS IS *SUMMER GLEESON* REPORTING LIVE--

--FROM THE CORNER OF SCHIFF AND MOLDOFF IN *DOWNTOWN GOTHAM--*

-- IN THE MIDST OF THE WORST CASE OF *GRIDLOCK* IN RECENT MEMORY--

--CAUSED *NOT* BY THE USUAL RUSH-HOUR TRAFFIC--

--BUT BY THOUSANDS OF *DISORIENTED* MOTORISTS AND PEDESTRIANS WHO SEEM TO BE *LOST--*

--AND BY *ACCIDENTS* CAUSED BY DRIVERS WHO ARE *DISOBEYING* POSTED DIRECTIONS OR SWERVING TO AVOID PEOPLE MILLING ABOUT AIMLESSLY--

NOW SHOWIN
COOL KILL

"-- BECAUSE THE *STREET SIGNS* HAVE BECOME *MEANINGLESS* TO THEM!"

YOU GOT IT, *TOO?*

YEAH! ONE MINUTE I WAS READIN' THE PAPER -- AN' THE NEXT, I COULDN'T MAKE OUT *NOTHIN!!*

APPARENTLY--INCREDIBLE AS IT MAY SEEM -- HUNDREDS UPON THOUSANDS OF GOTHAMITES ARE SUDDENLY AND INEXPLICABLY *LOSING THE ABILITY TO READ!*

I--I CAN'T *REMEMBER...!* I KNOW I *USED* TO KNOW HOW...

FIRST BAN OF GOTHA

...BUT I *CAN'T* ANYMORE! IT'S LIKE A PART OF MY BRAIN *BURNED OUT* OR SUMPIN'...!

BUSINESS ALL OVER THE CITY, AS WELL AS *PUBLIC TRANSPORTATION* AND MANY *OTHER* MUNICIPAL SERVICES HAVE BEEN THROWN INTO DISARRAY--

-- AND SOME MAY BE FORCED TO *SHUT DOWN* ALTOGETHER UNTIL THE CAUSE OF THIS BIZARRE PHENOMENON IS DISCOVERED AND ITS EFFECTS *REVERSED.*

NOW BACK TO DIRK BRICKER IN THE *WGBS* NEWSROOM. DIRK...?

THANK YOU, SUMMER. WE'LL CONTINUE WITH OUR ONGOING COVERAGE OF THE STRANGE *CRISIS* GRIPPING GOTHAM IN JUST A MOMENT.

BUT RIGHT NOW, THESE OTHER HEADLINES AT THE TOP OF THE NEWS: MAYOR HILL HAS...

...CALLED A PRESS CONFERENCE...

CALLED A PRESS CONFERENCE TO ANNOUNCE THE FORMATION OF A COALITION THAT WILL

...TO... TO...

...TO...

PLEASE STAND BY

MY WORD...!

ATTENTION, GOTHAMITES! -- THIS IS THE ARCHITECT OF YOUR CITY'S *NEW ORDER*, BREAKING IN ON REGULAR TV- AND RADIO TRANSMISSIONS FOR A BRIEF ANNOUNCEMENT.

PLEASE STAND BY

NOT THAT THERE WILL *BE* REGULAR TRANSMISSIONS FOR MUCH LONGER.

YOU SEE, THE TECHNICIANS CAN'T KNOW WHAT *TAPES* TO BROADCAST, OR WHICH *BUTTONS* TO *PUSH*, IF THEY *CAN'T READ* THE *LABELS* ON THEM!

NOW, AS YOU FACE THE VIRTUAL *END* OF LIFE AS YOU *KNOW* IT... I WANT TO TELL YOU *WHO* YOU HAVE TO THANK FOR THAT: *YOURSELVES!*

AFTER ALL, YOU LOW-BROWED LITTLE VERMIN, *YOU* ELECTED YOUR CRETINOUS *MAYOR HILL* AND A CITY COUNCIL FULL OF *MORONS* -- -- *NONE* OF WHOM HAS MADE A *PRIORITY* OF *EDUCATING* YOUR YOUTH!

LIBRARY

CLOSED UNTIL FURTHER NOTICE

AND *YOU* REFUSED TO PAY MORE *TAXES* TO IMPROVE YOUR *SCHOOL SYSTEM.* IN SO DOING, YOU HAVE *ENRAGED* ME.

HOW AND *WHY* IS UNIMPORTANT -- SUFFICE IT TO SAY I NOW PURSUE MY *JUSTICE...*

-- AND AT THE SAME TIME GIVE YOU A TASTE OF WHAT THE *FUTURE* HOLDS -- IF YOU CONTINUE DOWN THE PATH OF THE *YAHOO.*

I CAN PROMISE GOTHAM'S RULING CLASS THAT ITS *WORST NIGHTMARES* WILL COME *TRUE* --

--UNLESS IT AGREES TO PAY THE *RANSOM* I'VE DEMANDED--

BEGGING YOUR PARDON, MASTER BRUCE, I SHOULDN'T WISH TO *DISTURB* YOU...

ALFRED, I FEEL AS IF EVERY MUSCLE IN MY BODY HAS BEEN PULLED THROUGH A *PAPER-SHREDDER.*

I SHOULDN'T WONDER...

...YOU HAD QUITE A BUSY NIGHT EVEN *BEFORE* YOU SAVED THOSE TRAIN PASSENGERS.

"BUSY"? YOU COULD SAY THAT.

DO YOU HAVE ANY IDEA WHAT IT FEELS LIKE TO GO UP AGAINST A GUY WHO CAN TURN HIS *HANDS* INTO *ANVILS* BEFORE HE *PUNCHES* YOU?

ah, YES... *CLAYFACE.* NASTY BUSINESS, THAT.

HOWEVER --

THEN AT LEAST LET ME *TRY* TO GET A FEW HOURS' SLEEP, WILL YOU?

VERY GOOD, SIR. MIGHT I SUGGEST YOU TURN ON THE TELLY WITH THE SLEEPTIMER ON? IT MIGHT *RELAX* YOU.

KLIK

ALFRED! ALFRED, YOU'RE --

--FOR ONLY *I* HAVE THE *ANTIDOTE* TO YOUR *"ILLITERACY DISEASE"!*

-- MUCH TOO GOOD AT FOLLOWING THE ORDERS I GIVE YOU.

"I'VE ALREADY DELIVERED MY INSTRUCTIONS TO YOUR MAYOR HILL--ON AUDIO CASSETTE, OF COURSE...

ARE THE EFFECTS *PERMANENT*?

YES.

REEEEEEEE KLIK

THE *DAMAGE* THIS THING'LL DO IS *INCALCULABLE*.

WHOK WHOK

TELL ME ABOUT IT! I'VE GOT EVERY AVAILABLE MAN ON THE STREET, HAMILTON-- AND NOT ONLY MY RESOURCES--

--BUT ALSO THE *FIRE DEPARTMENT'S* ARE BEING STRETCHED TO THE *LIMIT* JUST COPING WITH ALL THE *ACCIDENTS!*

THE MINUTE THE CRIMINAL ELEMENT SEES THAT THE FORCE IS *VULNERABLE*, IT'LL BE A *FREE-FOR-ALL* OUT THERE!

WHOKWHOKWHOK

I AGREE. THE AMOUNT THIS GUY'S ASKING FOR IS *NOTHING* COMPARED TO THE COST OF POTENTIAL DAMAGE--

--OR OF TRYING TO *REEDUCATE* OUR KEY PERSONNEL... AND THE EXTORTIONIST *KNOWS* IT.

REEEEEEEE

DO YOU *HAVE* TO DO THAT *NOW*?

REEEEEEE

SORREE, MISTA MAYOR... ALL I KNOW'S I GOT A WORK ORDER TO *FIX* THIS THING. BUT DON'T SWEAT IT-- I'M *DONE*.

AS I WAS SAYING, GENTLEMEN... I'M RECOMMENDING THAT SOMEHOW WE *FIND* THE MONEY TO *PAY* THE RANSOM...

...BEFORE *MASS HYSTERIA* AND *RIOTING* REDUCE OUR CITY TO *RUBBLE!*

COBRA

ACT TWO "HELP ON THE WING"

UNABLE TO SLEEP, SIR...?

YOU SAW TO THAT. AND THANK YOU.

ABOUT THIS... "ILLITERACY PLAGUE," SIR. WHATEVER DO YOU SUPPOSE THE CAUSE MIGHT BE?-- MASS HYPNOSIS? A DRUG IN THE WATER SUPPLY?--

--SOME KIND OF GAS?

ANY OF THOSE IS POSSIBLE. MY GUESS IS THAT IT SPREADS BY AN AIRBORNE VECTOR WITH A FAIRLY LIMITED RANGE--

--SINCE NEITHER OF US HAS BEEN AFFECTED-- UP HERE ON THE ESTATE, OVERLOOKING THE CITY.

THEN MIGHT I SUGGEST, SIR...

...IF YOU ARE CONTEMPLATING ASSISTING IN QUELLING THE VARIOUS DISTURBANCES ARISING IN THE CITY, FROM THE SAFETY OF THE BATWING--

THAT'S EXACTLY WHAT I'M THINKING.

--THAT YOU TAKE THE PRECAUTION OF WEARING A GAS MASK...?

DONE. OH, AND, ALFRED ...?

DON'T WAIT DINNER.

GOTHAM STATE UNIVERSITY

HEY, GRAYSON-- YOU'RE NOT HEADIN' TO YOUR *EIGHT O'CLOCK*, ARE YOU?

WELL...*YEAH.* ANY REASON I *SHOULDN'T* BE?

WHERE'VE *YOU* BEEN? ALL CLASSES HAVE BEEN *SUSPENDED--INDEFINITELY!*

THAT *"CAN'T-READ"* THING THAT'S GOING AROUND...?

YEAH--THEY SAY 1 OUT OF 3 PEOPLE AROUND HERE *HAS* IT.

*hmm...*WITH *THOSE* NUMBERS, TURNING ON THE *LIGHTS* IN THE *CLASSROOM* ISN'T WORTH THE *ELECTRIC BILL.*

YOU GOT *THAT* RIGHT. THEY SAY THIS PLACE IS GONNA BE A *GHOST-TOWN* BY TOMORROW MORNING.

NO POINT HANGING AROUND *HERE* EATING *DORM FOOD,* THEN--

"--NOT WHEN YOU CAN CALL 'WAYNE MANOR' HOME."

whoa.

21

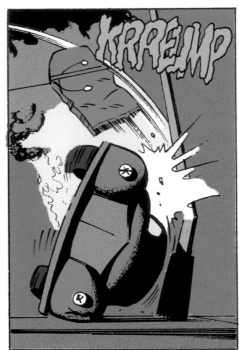

KRRRIMP

BWAAROOM

"THE WORST FEARS OF LAW ENFORCEMENT OFFICIALS ARE BEING REALIZED AT THIS HOUR--

"--AS ISOLATED OUTBREAKS OF *MOB VIOLENCE* AND *LOOTING* ARE BEING REPORTED IN VARIOUS NEIGHBORHOODS.

" IN THE *ROBINSON DISTRICT,* AN *ALTERCATION* BETWEEN *MOTORISTS* STUCK IN AN INTERSECTION THERE HAS *ESCALATED*--

"-- INTO A *LARGE-SCALE BRAWL* IN WHICH SEVERAL SHOP WINDOWS WERE BROKEN--

"-- AND NOW EYEWITNESSES ARE REPORTING *LOOTERS* MAKING OFF WITH *THOUSANDS OF DOLLARS* IN *MERCHANDISE* FROM THOSE STORES, AS CALLS TO *POLICE* GO *UNANSWERED.*

"SPOKESPERSONS FOR BOTH THE POLICE AND FIRE DEPARTMENTS--

"--CONFIRM A RECORD NUMBER OF CALLS FOR ASSISTANCE--

"--DUE TO THE HEIGHTENING STATE OF EMERGENCY--

KABAMM

WHUMP

JEWELS ·R· US

"--BUT DENY THAT THE DEMANDS FOR HELP--

"--EXCEED THE NUMBER OF PERSONNEL AVAILABLE TO RESPOND!"

uh...

...uh...

25

AN' IF *I* WUZ *YOU*, I'D BE GETTIN' SOME NEW *TEETH*!

HUH?

ASK ABOUT OUR CONVENIENT LAYAWAY PLAN

HUH??!

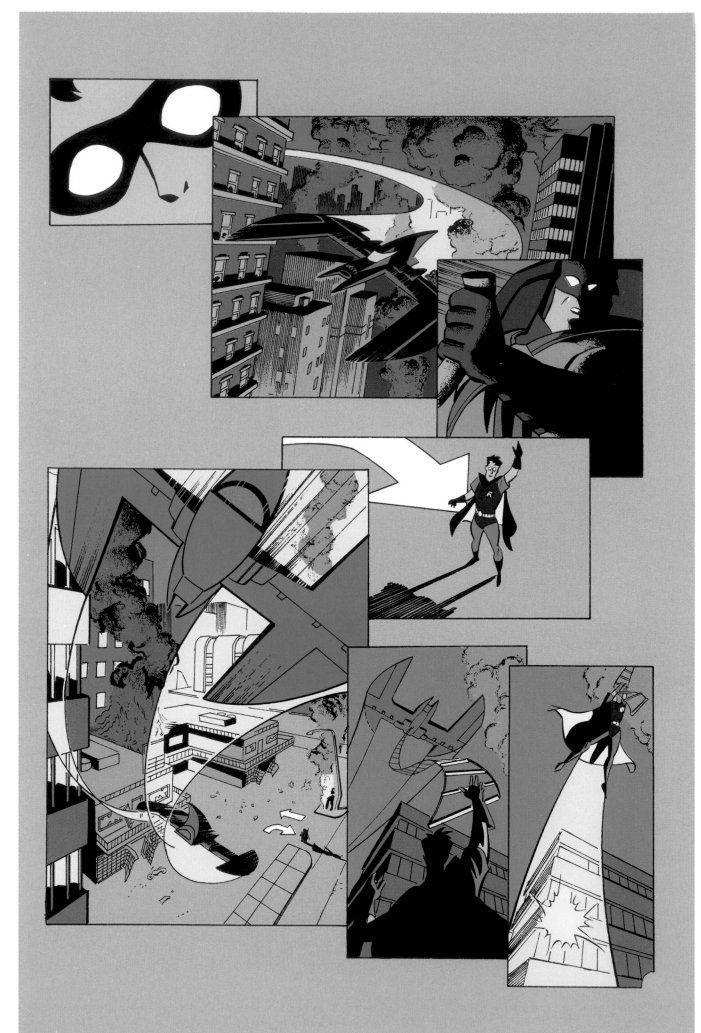

NEXT TIME YOU NEED ME TO *PICK YOU UP* SOMEWHERE, KID, *CALL AHEAD* FIRST, WILL YOU?

VERY FUNNY, BRUCE.

SERIOUSLY, MASTER DICK... HOW ARE YOU FEELING?

ASIDE FROM A SUDDEN *DIP* IN MY *READING-COMPREHENSON SKILLS?* NEVER BETTER, ALFRED.

THAT'S GOOD. NOW, IF ONLY YOU HAD SOME CLUE AS TO HOW *YOU* CAUGHT THIS "ILLITERACY BUG"!..

THERE'S NO WAY I CAN BE *SURE* OF THIS, BUT I *THINK* IT MIGHT BE *TRANSMITTED*--LIKE A *BROADCAST* SIGNAL.

WHAT MAKES YOU SAY THAT?

WELL...I KNOW THIS SOUNDS CRAZY, BUT I THOUGHT I SAW GUYS IN THAT ELECTRONICS STORE WHO *WEREN'T* LOOTING IT...

... BUT WERE ACTUALLY *PLANTING TV'S* AND STEREOS AND STUFF IN THE STORE--FOR *OTHERS* TO *STEAL.*

MAYBE THESE GUYS ARE DISTRIBUTING *"DOCTORED"* EQUIPMENT THROUGHOUT THE CITY...

I *GET* IT. OKAY, LET'S ASSUME IT'S *NOT "CRAZY."* NOTICE ANY-THING TO HELP "MAKE" THESE GUYS?

ACTUALLY, YEAH... THEY WERE ALL WEARING "COLORS"--THEY WERE *SNAKES.*

THE *STREET GANG...?*

BEGGING YOUR PARDON, SIR... BUT THAT *TAPE* YOU MADE OF THE *EXTORTIONIST'S* BROADCAST...?

I'VE RUN IT THROUGH THE *VOICE-ANALYSIS* PROGRAM, AS YOU REQUESTED, SIR.

THE EXTORTIONIST'S *VOICE-PRINT* DOES INDEED *MATCH* THAT OF PRECISELY THE FELON YOU *SUSPECTED.*

FIGURES. IF THE PERP IS WHO WE *THINK* IT IS, HE'S JUST THE SORT TO CONCOCT SO CYNICALLY CLEVER A PLAN:

HE PROBABLY CHOSE *GANG MEMBERS* AS *HENCHMEN* THINKING *THEY* WOULDN'T BE DISTRACTED BY HIS... WHATEVER-IT-IS --

"-- BECAUSE THEY PROBABLY *CAN'T READ* TO BEGIN WITH!"

I'M SURE IT'S NOW ONLY A MATTER OF HOURS *BEFORE* THEY'LL START ARRANGING FOR DELIVERY OF THE *RANSOM!*

WE'LL *SEE.* HOW DO YA KNOW THEY'LL BE *ABLE* TO GET IT TOGETHER?

DON'T WORRY, MARIO... IT'S ONLY *WORDS* THEY CAN'T READ. *NUMBERS* ARE STILL *NUMBERS* TO THEM-- I MADE SURE OF *THAT!*

YOU SEE, AS LONG AS THEY COULD TELL THEMSELVES IT WAS JUST A BUNCH OF NAMELESS, FACELESS *"LITTLE PEOPLE"* WHO WERE CATCHING *"THE DISEASE"*... THE POWERS THAT BE WOULDN'T TAKE IT *SERIOUSLY.*

BUT THAT WAS *BEFORE* YOU MADE SURE THAT THE NEXT TIME *MAYOR HILL* TRIES TO *LIE* TO THE PUBLIC ABOUT THE SEVERITY OF THE PROBLEM...

...HE *WON'T BE ABLE TO READ* THE TEXT OF HIS *OWN* FLATULENT *SPEECH!*

BELIEVE ME-- *THAT* WILL PROVIDE THE KIND OF *TERROR* THAT'LL GET A *RESPONSE* OUT OF THESE PEOPLE!...

...AND SHOW THEM ONCE AND FOR ALL THAT *TERROR* IS THE NAME OF THE GAME IF THEY DARE *DEFY*...

30

A

B

C

D

WHO AM I?

Take a look at these shadows! can you work out which character they belong to?

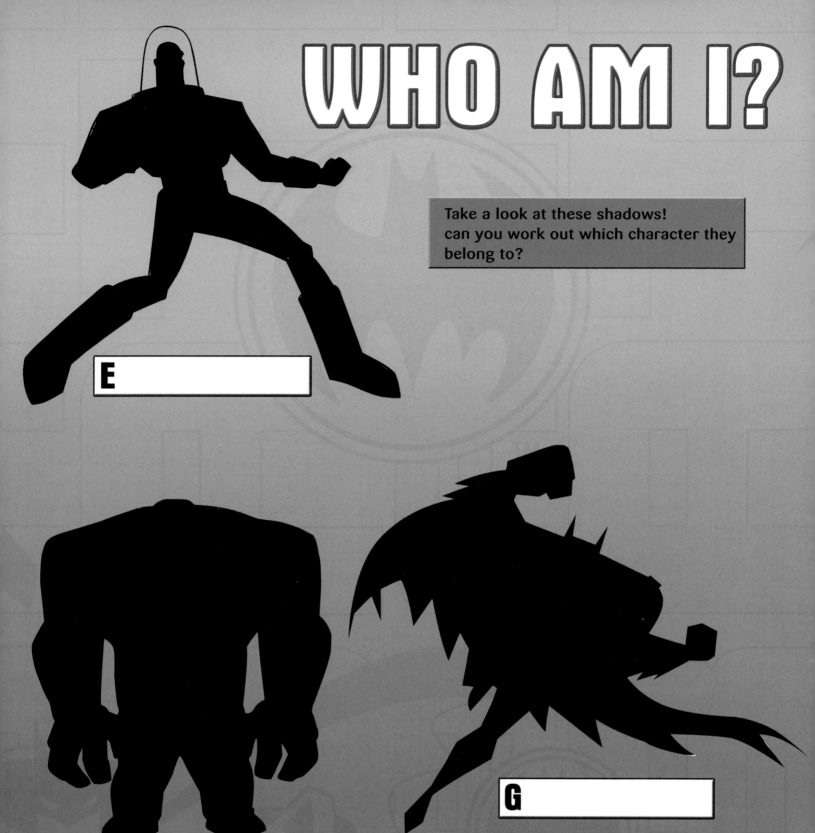

E [ ]

F [ ]

G [ ]

HOW TO DRAW
SCARECROW

Using the grid as a guide, copy the picture of scarecrow on the left, square by square, into the box. When you have finished colour your picture to match.

STOP WHINING! YOU GUYS SOUND LIKE OLD WOMEN.

WHOLESALE PRICES!!

CIRO'S CIRCUIT SHA

BUT THE SCARECROW'S PLAN IS WORKIN'! THIS STUFF'S ALREADY MADE HALF THE CITY...uhh...

ILLITERATE.

...RIGHT! SO WHY DO WE HAVE TO KEEP PUTTING IT IN THE STORES?

BECAUSE, STUPID, THE MAYOR HASN'T SAID HE'LL PAY SCARECROW THE MONEY FOR THE ANTIDOTE. AND IF HE DON'T GET PAID, *WE* DON'T GET PAID. SO MOVE IT!

HEY, MARIO, I CAN'T SEE A THING IN HERE, MAN.

YEAH, WHAT'S UP WITH THE LIGHT?

HOLD ON...

YOU KNOW WHAT TO DO?

CHECK.

LET'S SEE WHAT MAKES YOU TICK...

OH NO. NO. NOT AGAIN. PLEASE!

EVERY TIME THE SAME DREAM OVER AND OVER AND OVER AGAIN! *NO MORE!*

PLEASE CALM DOWN, PROFESSOR CRANE. YOU ARE NOT DREAMING. YOU'RE IN ARKHAM ASYLUM, WHERE YOU'VE BEEN FOR SOME TIME.

NOT... NOT A DREAM?

NOT AT ALL, EXCEPT MAYBE A "DREAM-COME-TRUE"! YOU SEE, WE'RE HERE TO OFFER YOU A GREAT OPPORTUNITY, PROFESSOR CRANE.

GREAT OPPORTUNITY.

HOW WOULD YOU LIKE TO *TEACH* AGAIN?

TEACH?

YES. IT'S PART OF A NEW "WORK-RELEASE" THERAPY WE'RE EXPERIMENTING WITH. YOU'LL BE TAKEN TO A LOCAL COLLEGE TWICE A WEEK TO TEACH A COURSE ON THE SUBJECT OF YOUR CHOICE.

YOUR CHOICE.

IT'S BEEN SO LONG...

FOOLS! THE SCARECROW IS NOT INTERESTED IN *LEARNING!* ONLY FEAR! *FEAR!* FEEEAAA... *mmpph!*

YES, SIR. I'D LIKE TO TEACH AGAIN.

CAN'T READ, CAN'T WRITE. PRODUCTS OF A SYSTEM GONE WRONG. YOU CAN'T TEACH THEM ANYTHING.

BUT YOU CAN TEACH THE SYSTEM A LESSON. A LESSON IN *FEAR!*

YES.

YES.

NO!

HUH?

I SAID WE GOT ANOTHER BUNCHA TV'S ALL WIRED UP AND READY TO GO, SCARECROW.

GOOD. SEND THEM OUT.

WE'LL TEACH THEM *ALL* A LESSON.

THERE'S BEEN A LOT OF TALK, A LOT OF CONFUSION AND A WHOLE LOT OF HOOPLA SURROUNDING THIS WHOLE ILLITERACY THING, AND AS YOUR MAYOR I'M HERE TO PUT A STOP TO IT.

FIRST OFF, THIS SO-CALLED "DISEASE" IS THE RESULT OF AN ELECTRONIC GIZMO HIDDEN INSIDE YOUR STEREOS AND TV'S. WITH A SCREWDRIVER AND A LITTLE PATIENCE, YOU CAN REMOVE IT YOURSELF WITHOUT DAMAGING YOUR VALUABLE EQUIPMENT.

SECONDLY, THE "MYSTERY MAN" WHO IS *OH-SO-QUICK* TO CRITICIZE THIS ADMINISTRATION'S *EXEMPLARY* RECORD ON EDUCATION IS A CRIMINAL MANIAC NAMED JONATHAN CRANE...

SCARECROW!

SKKRASH

CAN YOU SPOT THE

Here are two pictures. They might look the same but there 10 things that are different about them. How many can you find? When you spot one circle it with a pen or pencil.

HEROES ON THE MOVE

DIFFERENCE?

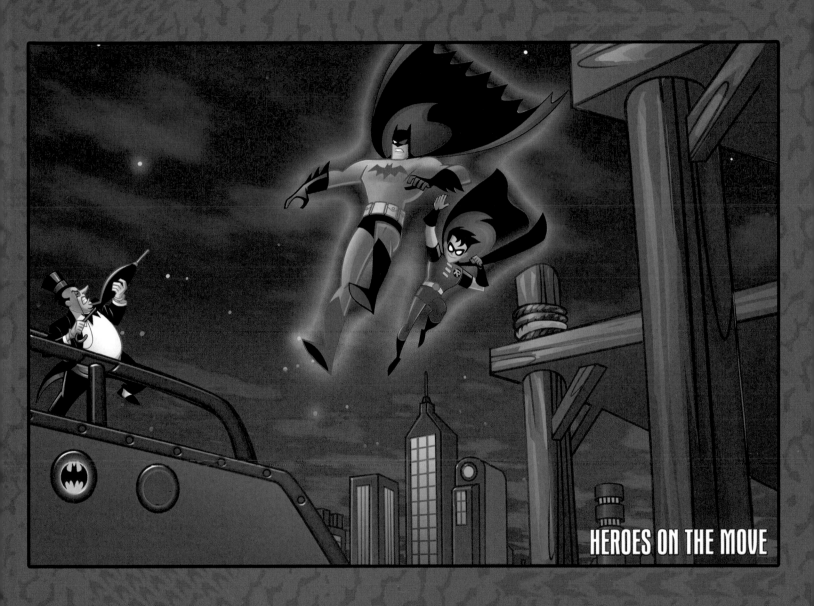

HEROES ON THE MOVE

BATMAN AND ROBIN

CRIME SOLVER CLUB

SEEK AND FIND!

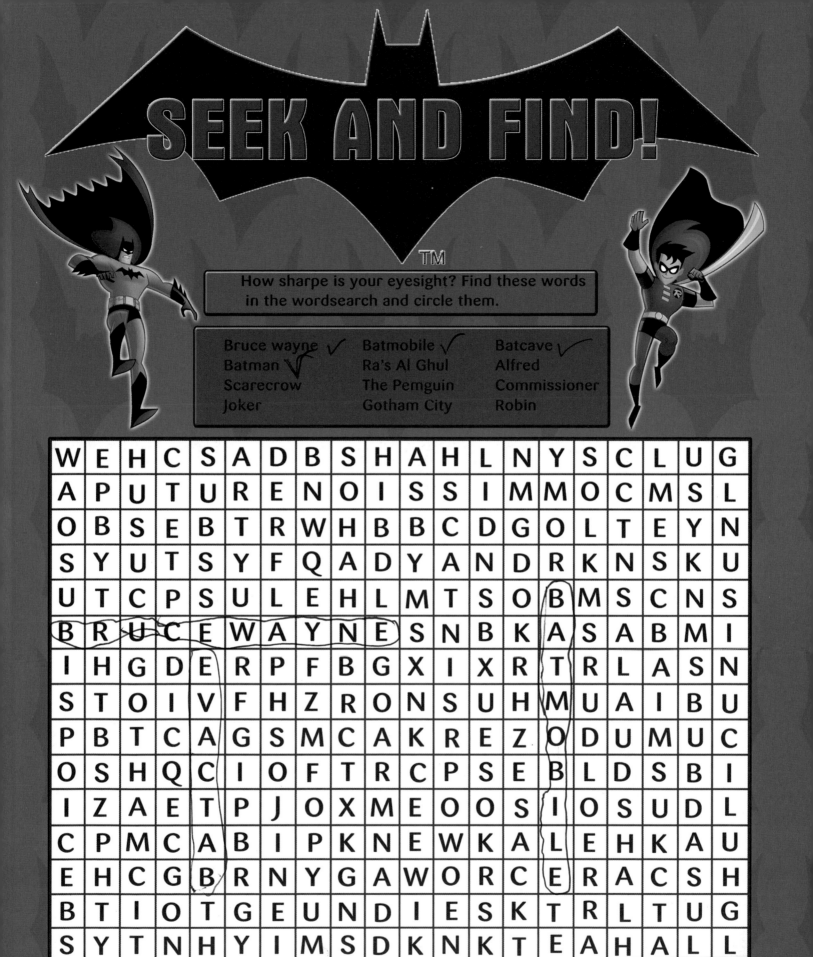

How sharpe is your eyesight? Find these words in the wordsearch and circle them.

Bruce wayne ✓	Batmobile ✓	Batcave ✓
Batman ✓	Ra's Al Ghul	Alfred
Scarecrow	The Pemguin	Commissioner
Joker	Gotham City	Robin

W	E	H	C	S	A	D	B	S	H	A	H	L	N	Y	S	C	L	U	G	
A	P	U	T	U	R	E	N	O	I	S	S	I	M	M	O	C	M	S	L	
O	B	S	E	B	T	R	W	H	B	B	C	D	G	O	L	T	E	Y	N	
S	Y	U	T	S	Y	F	Q	A	D	Y	A	N	D	R	K	N	S	K	U	
U	T	C	P	S	U	L	E	H	L	M	T	S	O	B	M	S	C	N	S	
B	R	U	C	E	W	A	Y	N	E	S	N	B	K	A	S	A	B	M	I	
I	H	G	D	E	R	P	F	B	G	X	I	X	R	T	R	L	A	S	N	
S	T	O	I	V	F	H	Z	R	O	N	S	U	H	M	U	A	I	B	U	
P	B	T	C	A	G	S	M	C	A	K	R	E	Z	O	D	U	M	U	C	
O	S	H	Q	C	I	O	F	T	R	C	P	S	E	B	L	D	S	B	I	
I	Z	A	E	T	P	J	O	X	M	E	O	O	S	I	O	S	U	D	L	
C	P	M	C	A	B	I	P	K	N	E	W	K	A	L	E	H	K	A	U	
E	H	C	G	B	R	N	Y	G	A	W	O	R	C	E	R	A	C	S	H	
B	T	I	O	T	G	E	U	N	D	I	E	S	K	T	R	L	T	U	G	
S	Y	T	N	H	Y	I	M	S	D	K	N	K	T	E	A	H	A	L	L	
P	D	Y	O	D	N	C	K	M	A	P	I	A	K	S	N	I	M	P	A	
X	P	J	K	M	E	Y	E	S	O	M	L	O	M	U	A	J	S	J	S	
E	N	M	B	A	T	M	A	N	A	S	J	E	S	S	K	B	T	G	A	
Z	G	T	L	E	K	O	A	L	M	B	L	I	U	T	N	O	G	E	R